THE GUY WHW N the TOUR de FRANCE

Other books by Martyn Turner

The Book (1983)
Illuminations (1986)
Not Viking Likely (1987)
A Fistful of Dailers (1987) Gill and Macmillan
Heavy Weather (1989) Gill and Macmillan

Thanks to Seamus Martin, Jean Turner and Terry Willers for the usual advice, help, aid, assistance, succour, photographs, drawings and literary stuff.

THE GUY WH◯ W◯N the TOUR de FRANCE

Political Cartoons 1987-1991

by
Martyn Turner

GILL AND MACMILLAN

Published in Ireland by
Gill and Macmillan Ltd
Goldenbridge
Dublin 8
with associated companies in
Auckland, Delhi, Gaborone, Hamburg, Harare,
Hong Kong, Johannesburg, Kuala Lumpur, Lagos, London,
Manzini, Melbourne, Mexico City, Nairobi,
New York, Sinagapore, Tokyo

© Martyn Turner 1991
0 7171 1916 5

Typeset by Seton Music Graphics, Bantry, Co. Cork
Origination by Hansa Graphics, Dublin
Printed by Criterion Press, Dublin

A CIP catalogue record for this book
is available from the British Library

Contents

Twenty Years Ago Today   7

Home Thoughts   14

The Tallaght Strategy   16

Education   18

Strikes   20

Hair Today   22

The Senate   24

Dailers   26

Greenery   36

The World   42

Bush Election   46

Economics   48

Third World   50

Central America   52

South Africa   56

People Who Live in Glasnosts   58

A Sporting Interlude   76

Northern Ireland   86

Condomania   100

An Election   102

The 48 Hour Rule   112

Finance   114

The Presidential Election   118

Lost Leaders   126

Mrs Thatcher   128

Speaking of Mad Cows   134

Justice   136

Anglo Irish Relations   138

The Gulf War   140

It Was Twenty Years Ago Today

Martyn Turner has been helping recently with enquiries. This is an edited version of the interview.

Q. I understand that this is the twentieth year of your drawings appearing in the *Irish Times*. My research suggests that the first drawing you had published in that journal was a single-column caricature of General Harry Tuzo, the then O/C of British troops in Northern Ireland. It appeared on 12 June 1971. Is that correct?

A. Yes.

Q. And twenty years on you are still able to satisfy this apparent fetish for drawing soldiers, terrorists, bombers and gunmen of all persuasions on a regular basis?

A. I am

Q. The person who gave you your first commission for the *Irish Times* was called Henry Kelly, is that right?

A. It is.

Q. And that subsequent to introducing you to the paper he felt obliged to leave serious journalism and become a host on obscure afternoon quiz shows in Britain?

A. He did.

Q. The second regular job you got on the *Irish Times* was with the Foreign News page. Was this much of a change from drawing soldiers, terrorists, bombers, gunmen and bloodthirsty politicians on the Northern page?

A. It was.

Q. In what way?

A. I was drawing *foreign* soldiers, terrorists, bombers, gunmen and bloodthirsty politicians.

Q. So, in fact, you spend your life drawing people for whom you have little or no regard and putting their portraits in front of thousands of readers, millions of readers if you include the 150 papers round the world that occasionally reprint your drawings. Do you feel you're actually enhancing the image of the very people you so dislike?

A. Have you seen the way I draw?

Q. Point taken. I understand you were brought up in a closed, backward society where there was a taboo on public discussion of sexual matters.

A. Yes.

An Early Soldier

A More Recent Soldier

Q. So when you moved to the Republic of Ireland in 1976 the debate and awareness in our free and uninhibited society down here must have come as something of a shock?

A. It was different, certainly.

Q. Is it true that before our great abortion debate you were totally unaware of what a zygote was?

A. Yes.

Q. And that you had never conceived in your wildest dreams of the multifarious uses and abuses of the humble condom before the great debates of '81, '86, '87 and '91?

A. Didn't have a clue.

Q. I understand that before a bishop kindly pointed it out to you that you hadn't realised that condoms could actually spread the AIDS virus rather than hinder its distribution.

A. I admit it.

Q. During the divorce debate you must have discovered that divorce leads to the undermining of society, the misery of children, the ejection of wives and children onto

8

the street penniless and uncared for, psychological damage on a vast scale for all those concerned not to mention the onset of plagues, pestilence and the wrath of god on all societies where divorce is legal?

A. It was news to me.

Q. You were entirely clueless as to the evils of divorce before you settled here?

A. I was.

Q. Your parents had never sat you down and explained all these things to you?

A. No.

Q. Why not?

A. They were divorced.

Q. This probably explains why someone with your education spends his life drawing silly pictures for a living.

A. Is that a question?

Q. Sad. My researchers tell me that at school and during third-level education you studied, among other things, politics. And that your education led you to believe that politics was about competing parties putting forward different policies and philosophies intended to lead to the good government of a country.

A. I did.

Q. But is it so that after 20 years of commenting on Irish politics you now realise the error of your ways?

A. I do.

Q. Can I now say that you appreciate that politics is really about what religion your parents were or whether your grandfather approved or disapproved of the wording of an oath?

A. You can.

Q. And furthermore do you now appreciate that a successful political party is not one that achieves its primary aims but is one that is able to change its views sufficiently at any given moment so that it can stay in power?

A. I do so appreciate, so I do.

Q. Would you agree with me then that Fianna Fail, founded on the twin premises of achieving national unity and encouraging the Irish language – two things that are now seemingly many centuries from achievement – can easily consider themselves as the most successful party in the history of the state?

Manager darts in and removes a Turner

By Renagh Holohan

A POSTER by the political cartoonist Martyn Turner, commissioned for the Art on the DART project, was pasted over on the order of a senior manager in Iarnrod Eireann immediately after the exhibition was opened at Pearse Station, Westland Row, Dublin, yesterday morning.

The 20-foot by 10-foot exhibit entitled "Election poster 988 AD" shows the Taoiseach, Mr Haughey, and the Minister for Finance, Mr MacSharry, dressed as Vikings and carried the caption "Vikings hurt the old, the sick and the handicapped". It was one of eight posters and six exhibits produced by various artists to mark the Dublin Millennium. The remaining seven posters are still on view at Pearse Station and the exhibits can be seen on DART trains.

LET'S be clear. There can be no justification for the withdrawal of a Martyn Turner poster from the Art on the DART exhibition at Pearse Station, Westland Row. To start even considering a justification is to speak the language of the censor. Art, like literature or journalism, has no value unless it is freely expressed. Having a democratic society means living with the consequences of free expression no matter how uncomfortable.

One would hope that other artists will show solidarity with Turner, as happened some years ago when a Rob Ballagh kite was suppressed by the Kilkenny Arts Week.

VIKING CUTS

Sir,—Regarding Martyn Turner's cartoon (November 3rd) commissioned by the clever DART Art Millennium poster display, may I comment that the greatest insult perceived or imagined was to compare the present Fianna Fail leadership to the Vikings. The Vikings were only in the ha'penny place. — Yours, etc.,
MARY McEVOY.
Quinn's Road,
Shankhill,
Co. Dublin.

* * *

Sir,—The removal by Iarnród Eireann of the Haughey-MacSharry cartoon from Pearse Station is to be applauded, for such a cartoon is deeply insulting and grossly offensive to Vikings. — Yours, etc.,
DERMOT P. CURRAN,
176 Sycamores,
Kilkenny.

'FF jibe' ban derails art

By JEROME REILLY

THE CENSORSHIP of a satirical cartoon featuring the Taoiseach Mr. Haughey and Finance Minister Ray MacSharry has led to a major row between Irish Rail and a number of the country's best known artists. The billboard-sized cartoon, from the nib of Martyn Turner, was blanked out last week by Irish Rail within hours of it being exhibited at Pearse Station as part of the "Art on the DART" scheme.

Now seven other artists have decided to withdraw their work which is also on display, in protest at the "blatant" censorship of Martyn Turner's work.

The cartoon itself depicts an axe-wielding Mr. Haughey with Minister MacSharry in Viking garb complete with helmets. The caption says: "Vikings hurt the old, sick and handicapped."

Irish Rail said it was their policy not to permit materials of a political nature to be displayed in their stations or on their premises.

Yesterday the Douglas Hyde Gallery said that, in protest at the move, they had requeted Irish Rail to remove the remaining works from the billboard project.

And last night an Irish Rail spokesman said they would agree to the Gallery's request to have the remaining works pasted over but with much regret.

The Perils of not sending work to The Irish Times

A. Who can dispute it?

Q. Why then, given the success and popularity of Fianna Fail, do you choose to criticise them regularly in your cartoons?

A. I'm funny that way.

Q. Are you? Your cartoons don't seem to be the funny sort.

A. No.

Q. I understand a priest once accosted you at a social gathering and asked if you had always been cynical.

A. He did.

Q. And he went on to ask if you planned to continue to be cynical.

A. He did.

Q. And, is it true that he then expressed the wish that you may continue to be cynical for the rest of your life?

A. Who am I to argue with the church?

Q. A politician, when making a speech opening one of your exhibitions, expressed the opinion that you were the greatest political cartoonist in the western world.

A. He did.

Q. But the same politician, 5 years later, when launching your last collection of political cartoons (still available at all good bookshops) said that at that time you were the greatest political cartoonist in the British Isles.

A. Who am I to argue with a politician?

Q. So in a short space of years, in the opinion of one political commentator you seem to have declined quite dramatically from the best in the western world to the best in the British Isles. Do you think that by now, five years further on, you are probably just the best in Kildare?

A. Possibly.

Q. Do you think that in view of this dramatic waning of powers you should turn your hand to other less demanding forms of art? Ones that don't require a new idea every day, perhaps, or don't have bits of caricatures or are in colour.

A. I tried that with Art on the Dart (see page 10)

*Some lines on the occasion of a
Ministerial speech at Mullingar*

While addressing the troops bold and handsome,
His pre-arranged speech overran some,
The T.D. from Louth,
Put his foot in his mouth
And spoke out the back of his transom.

An Archive Favourite

Q. Speaking of art and the Dart, I understand you weren't trained to do this sort of work, you rail against the world out of a naive vocational urge, you think it's your station in life to produce this constant stream of black and white art work, sometimes hitting and sometimes missing but always on time. Do you feel, sometimes, lucky to have the sort of platform provided for you by the *Irish Times*?

A. I couldn't have put it worse myself.

Q. Is it right that in 20 years or so of working for the *Irish Times* the number of messages and/or conversations with editors of that newspaper about the content, direction and manner of your cartoons can be counted on the fingers of one hand?

A. Yes.

Q. Why do you think this is?

A. I'm a lot taller and heavier than they are.

Q. It is 15 years since you left Northern Ireland. In that time do you think that things have changed? Do you accept that legislation has done as much as possible to redress the imbalances in, say, public employment practices and housing but that the inability of politicians to lead public opinion and the lack of imagination on the part of the terrorist community (coupled with the problems of dismantling the terrorism/industrial sector) to see anything other than the latest murder and the fact that it takes many generations to eliminate tribal bigotry is handicapping the emergence of a decent and pleasant community in Northern Ireland?

A. Yes.

Q. And do you find yourself, now you are integrated into the community of the republic of Ireland, sometimes going along with the popular consensus down here which says that Northern Ireland should just go away and that it's nothing to do with us.

A. Sometimes, yes.

Q. And is that attitude part of the problem of Northern Ireland?

A. It is.

Q. This year, 1991, sees the commemoration of the 75th Anniversary of the Easter Rising. How, at this moment, do you feel about Ireland?

A. At one with the leaders of the 1916 movement.

Q. But some of them were republicans, most of them were monarchists of some form or another, some were socialists, some were Catholic nationalists, some barely spoke English in an accent understandable to the general populace, some favoured violence, some opposed it, some changed their minds about rivers of blood when they actually saw some, some hoped that Germany would win the Great War, some were Ghandian pacifists, some were Gaelic supremacists. How can you be at one with them?

A. Well, like them, I'm pretty confused about Ireland most of the time.

Q. Thank you.

(Martyn Turner was, as usual, talking to himself.)

LETTERS TO THE EDITOR

Irish people still fighting to free their homeland

We will never forget the Holocaust and its atrocities.

However, let's give a moment to the Irish, of which I am a decendent, and their atrocities.

Their history also goes back thousands of years.

English leaders ordered the invasion of Eire. Babies were torn from their mother's breast and, with a swipe of the sword, the child was split in two. All people were found destroyed in this manner.

People had to go into the caves at night to hear Mass. Also, unable to speak their Gaelic tongue. "Erin-go-Braugh, Ireland forever."

They will fight until the seven counties are free.

Mrs. Marie Byrne Baker
Lake Worth

Someone Else, a writer to the Palm Beach Post, who is also pretty confused about Ireland

Home Thoughts

Random Portraits

**Brian Friel. Ian Paisley. John Wilson. Larry Goodman.
Charles J. Haughey. Eoghan Harris. Brendan Kennelly**

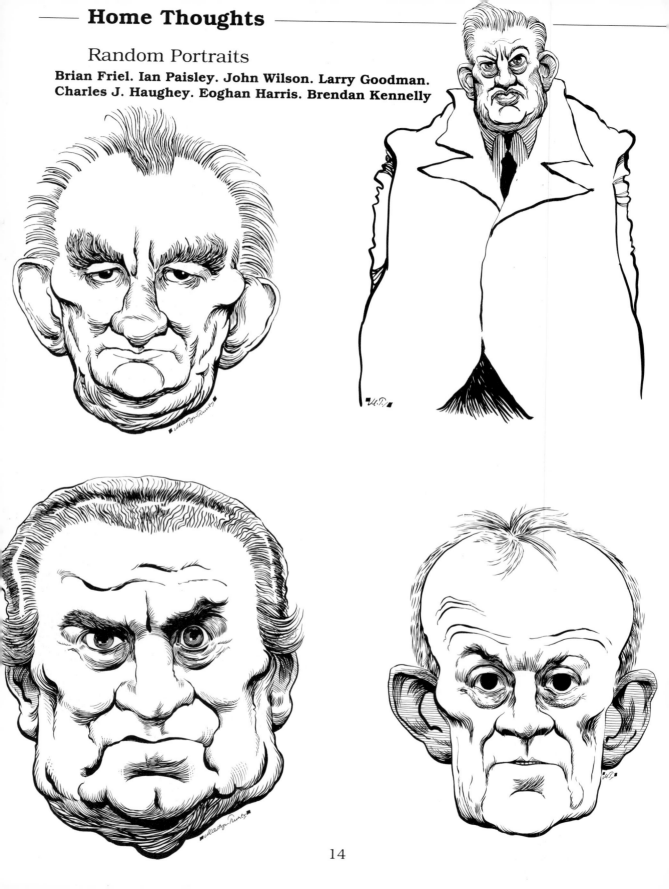

EXCLUSIVE

Special FULL COLOUR portrait in celebration of the "Green Presidency" of the E.C.

[Unfortunately Dublin smog may affect colour quality in some editions]

Guardian Angels For Dublin?- NEWS ITEM

17

Education Cuts: The First Signs

GREAT ACHIEVEMENTS FOR 1988 ... No. 1.

EDUCATION EXPLAINED No.1 The Pupil/Teacher Ratio...

This is a National school teacher. She (he)(it), as the case may be, has 30-40 minor beasts to teach and keep in some semblance of order. That's why she looks tired.

With a change in class size this teacher could have up to 20 more of the little b..b..b..babies to watch out for. She will need eyes in the back of her head. Hence, this is known as Increasing the pupil/teacher ratio......

EDUCATION EXPLAINED contd.

No.2. The Parent/Taoiseach ratio:

The statistical figure to be considered by politicians thinking of calling an early election..

suffer the children

mary mary quite..

NO TO CUTS

SKOOL

NO CUTS

DOWN WITH CUTS

3. Class Size:

In secondary education especially, the number of pupils in each form is directly related to the social class of the parents.

4. Leaving Certificate:

We can't all live on this island - official.

Nice knowing you. Please send money home

19

ESBOA CONSTRICTORS

PERHAPS SAINT PATRICK'S WORKING IN THE LABOUR COURT

BLACK OUTS : THE AREAS AFFECTED

ZONE Z
Management
Diplomacy
Flexibility

ZONE C
Common Sense
Political Reality
Generosity

ZONE A
Compassion
Practical Patriotism

STRANGE, BUT TRUE.

Saint Patrick could make snakes disappear from Ireland forever.........

...... but he can only make politicians disappear from Ireland for a long weekend.....

THIS WEEK...

The clocks go back...

the leaves finish falling from the trees...

final auditions for Father Christmas are completed...

the Dáil ends its summer holiday.....

Ho Ho Ho....

GETTING CAPPED THIS WEEK.

1 RTE Advertising   2 Pairings in the Dáil   3 David O'Leary

.....OF COURSE 3 IS JUST WISHFUL THINKING

The Latest Dramatic Incident in the Sovereignty of Our State

COMMEMORATIVE CRYSTAL CELEBRATING 30,000 EXTRA JOBS CREATED IN 89-90 IN IRELAND.

MADE IN GERMANY

PRECEDENCE:- Your Guide To Where You Stand In Line In Ireland

1ST President → 2ND (In Dublin) Lord Mayor → 3RD Taoiseach

1,747,292ND Non-Emergency Cases

2,352,531ST Unemployed

3,027,213RD Travellers

WE OUGHT TO HAVE A SYSTEM WHERE EVERYONE'S THE SAME...

LIKE A REPUBLIC?

THE PLANE PEOPLE of IRELAND

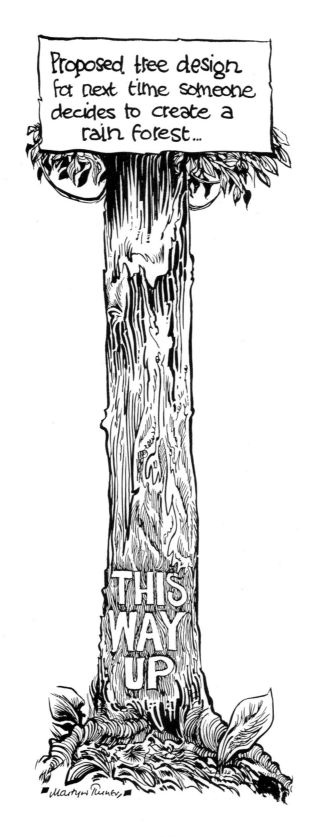

Random Portraits

Neil Kinnock. Fidel Castro. Nelson
Mandela. Dan Quayle. Helmut Kohl.
Boris Yeltsin. Lech Walesa.

HELMUT KOHL

HI! I'M DAN AND I'M 2ND IN COMMAND OF THE FREE WORLD

APRIL
APRIL 1
APRIL
APRIL

BORIS YELTSIN

SOLIDARNOSC

Censorship in the World.

Censorship in Iran.

In the Middle East, when in use, these weapons make the same sound...

AND IN NORTHERN IRELAND, TOO.

TIT FOR TAT TIT FOR TAT TIT FOR TAT

OLD
★BEAR★
NEW
TRICKS★

A Bush.   Campaign Image of A Bush.

46

He came from the South; the sun on his back. He was lean. He was tough. He was desperate.

Throughout the West bankers trembled at the mention of his name.

He had nothing to lose. An hombre on the edge.

He was Third World Man. The Man With No Money.

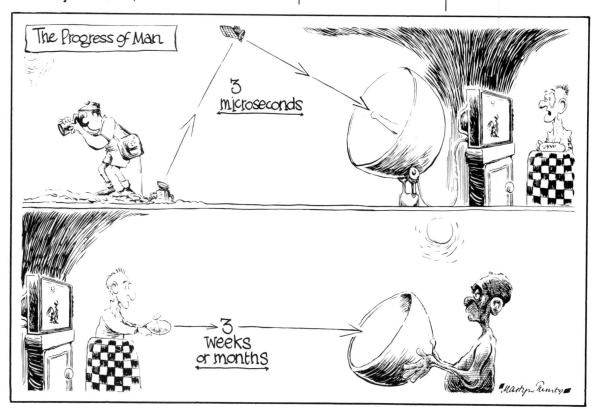

The Progress of Man

3 microseconds

3 weeks or months

52

HIS EX-MASTER'S VOICE

57

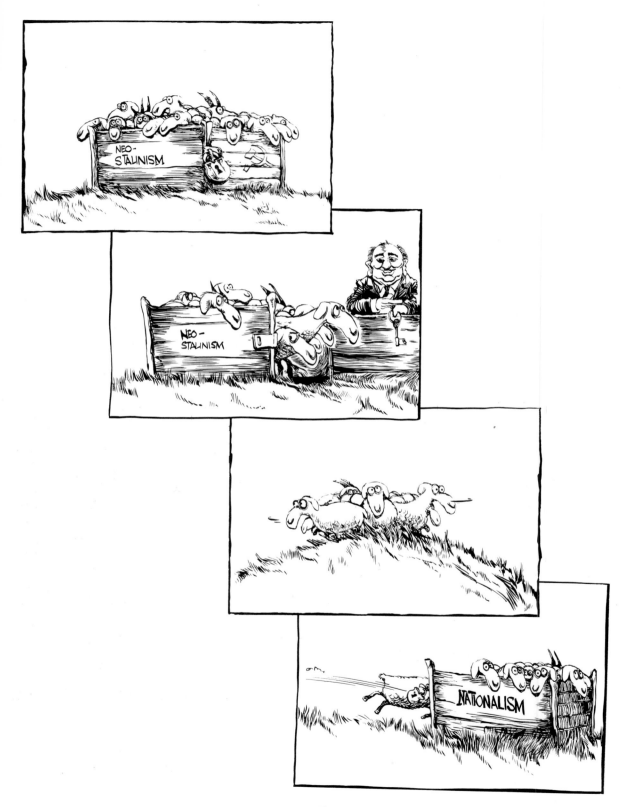

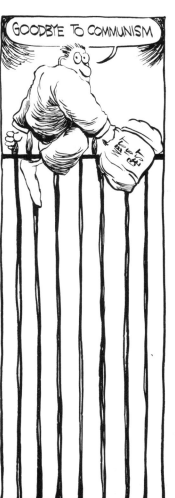

1950

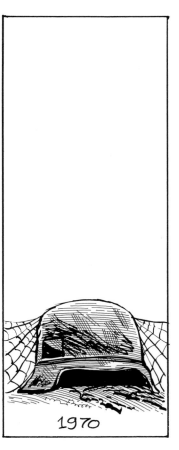

1970

1990

For one frightful moment Mikhael quite forgot where Namibia was.

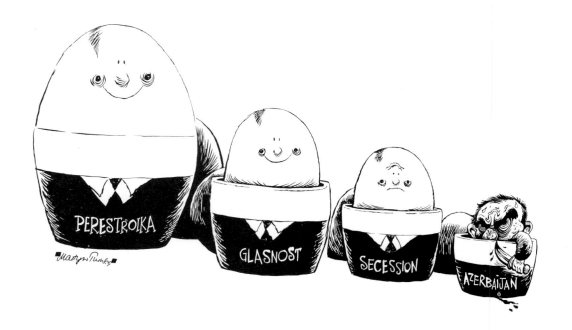

Mr Gorbachev learning about the Free Market Economy from the bottom...

Russian Food Dolls

74

1. Soccer

All Your World Cup Questions Answered

Q **Should I go on a special diet for the big match?**

A Medical opinion believes that a diet high in carbohydrates is the one most suitable for athletic pursuits that require stamina and energy. Those of you in Italy have a readymade form of this necessary food source in pasta. My personal favourite would be Pasta Al Funghi. Avoid, at all costs Pasta Sellby Date as this can lead to a bad dose of Italian tummy.

Q **Should we go with the sweeper throughout the match?**

A This makes no sense at all. The clearing up should be done long after the match and celebrations are over. Anyone trying to keep the floor clean during play can only cause irritation as he (or she) is bound to block someone's view of the telly.

Q **Who are the Italian dangermen?**

A Italy have been showing a united front since coming under the control of their trainer, Garibaldi. Many consider Canaletto the artist of the team, although he always has seemed to me a bit one-paced. Fellini, the Italian 8½ shirt, is grotesque but quite entertaining – he used to be a cartoonist, not many people know that. Mussolini's a dangerous right winger although a bit highly strung of late and Martini, while he can be shaken is rarely stirred. Watch out for Italy's answer to Ireland's Green Machine, Verdi.

Q **Should I sleep with my wife the night before the game?**

A This tricky and delicate question has met with different answers from different teams. It could be that Brazil, who were with their wives and girlfriends in Italy, made the wrong choice as they bowed out to the celibate Argentinians – or was it the other way round? Anyway on balance I would favour sleeping with one's spouse the night before the match. This is for two reasons. Firstly, sex before a match is a bad thing and sleeping with your wife may be the best way to avoid this. Secondly, if you plan to watch the match at home she may not let you in the house if you've been out all the night before.

Q **Our parrot is in extremely good health. If we lose to Italy how should I feel?**

A Parrot is actually an Old English corruption of the French word *pierrot*. So, in fact, you should feel as sick as a *pierrot*, which the dictionary describes as an "itinerant minstrel with a white face". So, you can either imagine you're an itinerant who's been refused entry into a pub to watch the match or you're a white man asking directions to a Klan meeting in Harlem. Either should bring the required level of nauseousness. The parrot quotation you are looking for, I believe, is "Nothing succeeds like a parrot with no teeth".

Q **My friends tell me that I lack bottle at critical moments around the box. Is there anything I can do to change this situation?**

A Your friends are simply trying to tell you to stop buying six packs and get a few barrels in. Under FIFA (Federation of Intoxicated Football Addicts) rules it is illegal not to have a drink in your hand when singing Olé. While on the subject remember the other new FIFA rules concerning dress – shirts should be worn outside the trousers at all times and socks, if you've remembered to put them on, should sag neatly below the ankles.

Q **I have noticed, during the summer months, that cartoonists in the *Irish Times* start writing pieces about golf and football and stop drawing cartoons. Is there a reason for this?**

A That's a very good question.

A FOOTBALL FAN'S GUIDE TO ITALIAN MONUMENTS...

BUILT FOR THE ITALIAN CUP FINAL OF 83 AD, THE COLOSSEUM (right) NEVER SURVIVED THE HAND TO HAND VANDALISM OF THE FIRST ALL DUTCH INTER-CITIES FAIRS CUP FINAL HELD TWO YEARS LATER....

THE STRAIGHT TOWER OF PISA (left) WAS ASSAULTED BY DEFEATED LEEDS UNITED SUPPORTERS RETURNING HOME FROM A FIRST LEG, 4TH ROUND, CHAMPION WINNERS CUP MATCH IN 1753. WHEN ASKED BY THE LOCAL POLICE WHY THEY DID IT THEY REPLIED; ARROGANTLY; "BECAUSE WE FELT SO INCLINED."

DAVE (right), THE FIRST SOCCER STREAKER, IS IMMORTALISED IN MARBLE AND CAN BE SEEN IN FLORENCE. HE WAS THE ONLY LIVELY THING IN THE FEBRUARY 1653 CLASH FIRENZE VERSUS PALERMO.

2. Golf
Putting Marx on Your Card

We recently had a guest from across the
water who devoted some portion of his visit
to regaling us with the wonders of
Thatcherism. Despite what I see as evidence
to the contrary, he assured us that a return
to primitive selfish economics was doing
Britain a power of good. "Hard work", he
said, "bicycle riding in search of same, etc.,
never did any harm. People are getting away
with too much. They're being mollycoddled."
Later in the week we went to play golf. We
reached the first green, a par five. I was 12
feet away after three shots. He was on the
edge of the green after four.

"How many shots are you giving me?",
he said.
"Shots!" I said, "Shots! I thought you were a Thatcherite!"
"What do you mean?" he said,
"Well," I expounded, "as I understand it you are a Thatcherite. You believe in Standing
On Your Own Two Feetedness. I happen to be a better golfer than you. My handicap,
at the last count, was 21 shots better than yours . . .
I wasn't born with a low handicap. It was achieved by the sweat of my brow. I spent
many, many days as a teenager slaving away on a golf course when I could have been
going to school, learning how to be a financier or playing snooker. I have callouses on
my hand from the thousands of shots I hit on the practice ground . . .
If I understand your present philosophy right you believe that it is open to everyone to
play off single figures. It only takes application, good old-fashioned hard work. If I
start giving you shots it would only encourage you in your slothfulness. Where would
the incentive be to better yourself? Why should I give you a hand out of shots just
because you happen to be, in the economics of golf, worse off than myself. I wouldn't
insult your dignity by feather-bedding you."
He tried to speak but I was in full flow now.
"You have opened my eyes," I said, "I now see the Handicapping System for what it is.
A socialist conspiracy intent on making us all equal. Merit on the golf course achieves
no reward. It seems to me that the Handicapping section of the GUI must be some
sort of front for Moscow. They must be, at the very least, members of the Workers'
Party or the Emmet Stagg wing of the Labour Party. I thank you. After 30 years I at
last realise that golf is a game played by capitalists but organised by communists.
I will have a new respect for those people in blazers with badges that run the whole
show."
"Is that a no?", he asked, "am I not getting any shots?".
"It's up to you", I said. "We can play it your way, survival of the fittest. Or we can play
according to the true revolutionary Marxist principles of the game and I will support
you, my weaker comrade. And anyway, I suppose I should be kind to my father."

On the second tee some ladies had been waiting patiently. Being mere women and seeing *men* approaching, they were waiting to let us through. The Revolution has a way to go yet, comrade golfers.

Putting on the Style

Two other members of the almost *Irish Times* Charity Fourball and Formation Dance Team, men of power and influence on the Sports pages, asked me to go to the Irish Open to find out about putting. Some subtle hint, eh. Next week the Editor will want me to go and see how an art school works. Putting is, of course, an art so it is natural that it is the one area of golf, at the moment, that is just simply bursting with creativity. Golf was never previously noted for its unconventionality. Change was positively frowned upon. I can still recall, a mere 25 years later, the problems I had trying to introduce beads, kaftans and waist length hair to the English game and the total disinterest shown by publishers to my book *Zen and the Art of Golf Course Maintenance*. Not only was dress and equipment required to be correct but even the manner in which one played had to conform. As a whipper-snapper I saw Dai Rees give a clinic. Dai Rees played with a two fisted grip but only late in his career came to admit it. When showing we punters how to play he would use the Vardon grip at address and at the end of his follow through, slip into the old two fister as he hit the ball. It has all changed. Changed utterly.

These days you're in trouble if you don't do anything peculiar. Professional golfers now appear to be better dressed versions of the lunatics of the Sunday morning fourball. Every week a new idea. This year they're all playing with gold shafted metal drivers and putting (at last, putting is mentioned) with an assortment of gardening implements, using an assortment of gardening techniques for motive power.

Of course when you're "putting for dough" it can put unnatural strain on the nervous system. The worst case was the American who became catatonic standing over a 12 foot putt on an 18th green and was, after five minutes had elapsed, carted off to the hospital stuck in the crouching position, putter glued into his hands. Thus at the Irish Open this week we have seen an assortment of schemes designed to keep the padded cell at bay and, since the proponents continue to make money and play successful golf have given the imprimatur for we lesser mortals to also do silly things on the green. Sam Torrance's four foot black thing is the obvious example. He got it specially made and then, of course, fiddled around with it a bit more and Bob's Your Uncle – in Torrance's case, Bob's Your Father. Strangely, even though the thing is specially made he still putts with the heel of the club well off the ground, a reverse Aoki position and, while he rests his chin on the end of the shaft there's no comfortable little chin shaped holder on the top. This technique has also been adopted by Peter Senior who had, until a few weeks ago, been a proponent of the hurling grip technique for both putting and chipping. Langer seems to have introduced a new variation in his putting which now takes on all the formality and artistry of the Japanese Tea Ceremony. On one green he putted from off the green conventionally (reverse overlap) after miming the shot with his right hand only a couple of times. He putted this way without his glove. For the next two putts he put on his glove and adopted the new right hand gripping left forearm techniques. I saw him later helping, discussing, the wonderful world of putting with the latest crazy recruit Eamon Darcy. Darcy has solved his problems by reversing his hands and getting a putter he calls a branding iron which is a flat triangle welded onto a very goose-necked shaft.

Given that Langer has suffered from and cured the yips countless times in his career it should be noted that the other two current problem putters, Eamon Darcy and Sam Torrance have something in common. They are the people who sank the winning putts in the last two Ryder Cups. If heroes like that have trouble putting why should the Occasional *Irish Times* Charity Fourball and Formation Dance Team expect me to be any better?

The Professional Way of Golf

There is something about a professional golfer, a certain *vous ne savez quoi*, that marks them out from the common herd who trample around the Irish Open spectating. You're probably wondering what it is. Well I'm going to tell you. (Free and independent thinkers among you should cut the rest of this article out, attend the Irish Open for at least 2 days, make your own mind up, and then refer back to see if you got the right answer.) As I'm not permitted, under Royal and Ancient *Irish Times* Rules, to give one word answers I'll tell you, first, to drag it out, what we all have in common with professional golfers.

TECHNIQUE. Your average weekend golfer can hit a golf ball as well as your average professional . . . once or twice in his life. This means that somewhere in that swishing loopy off balanced ritual dance you call a golf swing there lurks the means to propel the ball 260 yards off the tee, hit a five iron to 20 feet and hole the putt. You have that ability, the only thing you lack is the talent to do it nine times out of ten, or more likely for a professional, 39 times out of 40.

EQUIPMENT. In this paradise of a free market economy that we all call home we are as entitled as the next man to buy the very best equipment Scandinavians with funny little white goatee beards living in Arizona can invent. If you think Mr Ping (funny name for a Norwegian) makes putters that putt better, as most professionals do, then all you have to do is save five pounds each week for twelve weeks and go and buy one. Similarly with irons and woods, sorry, metals. Next year you'll be able to buy one of those drivers that Ray Floyd and Jack Nicklaus used in the Masters. You can already buy gold graphite and hot metal and all the other things that the professionals use because they think it makes them play better. That's another thing we have in common with the pros – when they play badly they often think it's something to do with the clubs, too. The days when Sam Snead would whittle a set of woods from a hickory tree in the morning, go out and break the course record with them in the afternoon and still have something over for fish and chips and a movie in the evening are long gone.

SOCIAL STANDING. Most professionals are just as poor as you and me. They have the same problems as us all. It is a little known fact, that will never be repeated anywhere else, that when I receive a modest fee from the *Irish Times* as recompense for writing (and drawing) this guff – I will have earned more from the Irish Open than the professional for whom I used to caddy. Apart from the millionaires the peleton of the circuit are just a bunch of self-employed folk desperate to keep their heads above water and wondering where the pension is going to come from. They aren't intellectual giants either, more *Daily Mirror* than *The Guardian* on the whole.

Their brains, intellectual or otherwise, don't function on a different plane emotionally from the rest of us. They all get panicky, nervous, terrified standing over 5 foot putts. They twitch, jerk and stutter and go to psychologists just to get themselves to the tee on time. The successful ones have a bit of charisma but that is probably true of successful people in every one of life's activities. So what is it that makes them so darned good and the rest of us so darned bad at the game?

The first theory I had was that to be a good golfer you had to have a single syllable name. Nick, Greg, Jack, Payne, Tom, Ray, Lee, old Sam and Ben and Ireland's own golfing genius, Fred. But whoa there, what about Severiano, Jose-Marie, Bernard, Curtis and Christy, not forgetting Christy. Far too many double syllables for comfort (there's Sandy, too and Ian). I think this theory can be sent somewhere deep in the left-hand rough.

Theory number 2 is the correct one. Check this against your own answer. The difference between us and them is that they all have year round sun tans and they all play golf in brand new clothes and shiny shoes. Very shiny shoes. When was the last time you saw one of us so attired? And the reason they all wear new clothes is that for the last few years professional golfers have really been fashion models. Half the sales from the pros shops now come from clothing. The touring pros model the clothes on the circuit. Like all models they are trained to be poised, balanced, to look calm and composed when they are really as uptight as hell and sweating bricks. They are, like all models, able to move rhythmically, to keep their heads still enough to balance a book on, and to not look embarrassed when they are wearing pink and mauve plus fours with a matching lime green and pina colada shirt.

Poise, balance, rhythm, stillness of the head, just like a fashion model – that's all you need to be able to play great golf . . . must try it sometime.

3. Croquet
Going Through The Hoops

I got a letter yesterday morning from a member of the supporters' club. He urged me "to stay my hand for a while" perchance a posse of enraged citizens, without the steam letting-off outlet of a political cartoon in the *Irish Times*, might take it upon themselves to "frogmarch" Diamond Chas to "the Anna Livia fountain and throw him in."

Not being one to stand in the way of a lynch mob and knowing a good excuse when I see one, I stopped drawing, hied it to the car, drove 37 miles, and went to watch croquet at Carrickmines.

For two summers now I've been croqueting, whenever possible, twice a week. I play on a lawn just up the road at a friend's place. Our abilities are such that I can claim that I usually beat him and he can claim that he usually beats me. He is, of course, playing at home in front of his own crowd (usually a cat and two very small dogs) and I, of course, feel a certain obligation to let him win as it involves his balls, his hoops, his lawn and his mallets.

Ball: 3⅝"
Hoop: 3¾"
Distance: 2'6"
Angle: 80°
Price of Beer: £1

We've never seen anybody else play croquet; thus a brief excursion to Carrickmines to see how it goes in the rest of the world.

Croquet is a wonderfully violent and evil game. I'm sure it was invented by Machiavelli. It is even better than political cartooning for letting off steam. You are allowed – obliged even – to knock your opponent's ball into the back of beyond. We do this, out here in the Kildare jungle, to the accompaniment of, at very least, a deep throated teehee – at most a full-blooded Indian yelp. They don't do that at Carrickmines. They pretend that knocking your opponent's ball into oblivion is part of a serious overall strategy.

What is more, they strategise in tennis whites. We do it in gardening clothes because one of us has just cut the grass.

I write this piece for two reasons. One is "to stay my hand" (take a day off). The other is to urge you to all look kindly upon croquet; it is a great game with a poor image. Go and see for yourself at Carrickmines (tournament on this week) or at Herbert Park. And try and liven them up a bit: whistle and shout when they play a good shot.

4. Cricket

5. Not Cricket

6. Rugby

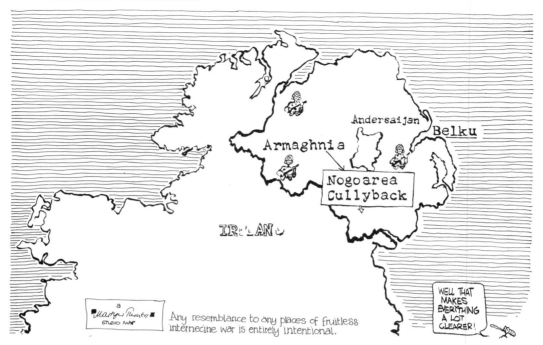

Andersaijan

Belku

Armaghnia

Nogoarea
Cullyback

IRELAND

a Martyn Turner STUDIO MAP

Any resemblance to any places of fruitless internecine war is entirely intentional.

WELL THAT MAKES EVERYTHING A LOT CLEARER!

MIND TEST extra
The Northern Ireland Problem

Solutions to; The Secretary of State for Northern Ireland, Stormont Castle or The Secretariat of the Anglo-Irish Agreement, Maryfield, Belfast, or any other interested party.

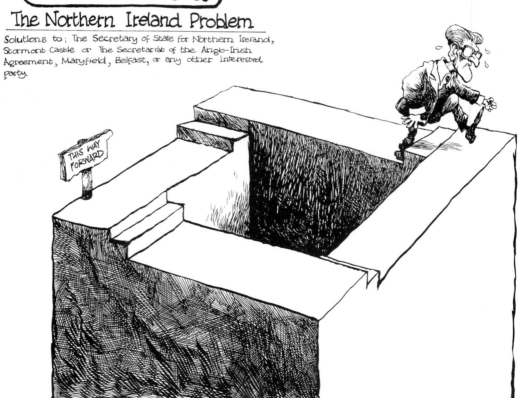

THIS WAY FORWARD

☆ FOR OUR AMERICAN VISITORS ☆

The Northern Ireland problem explained in your own language

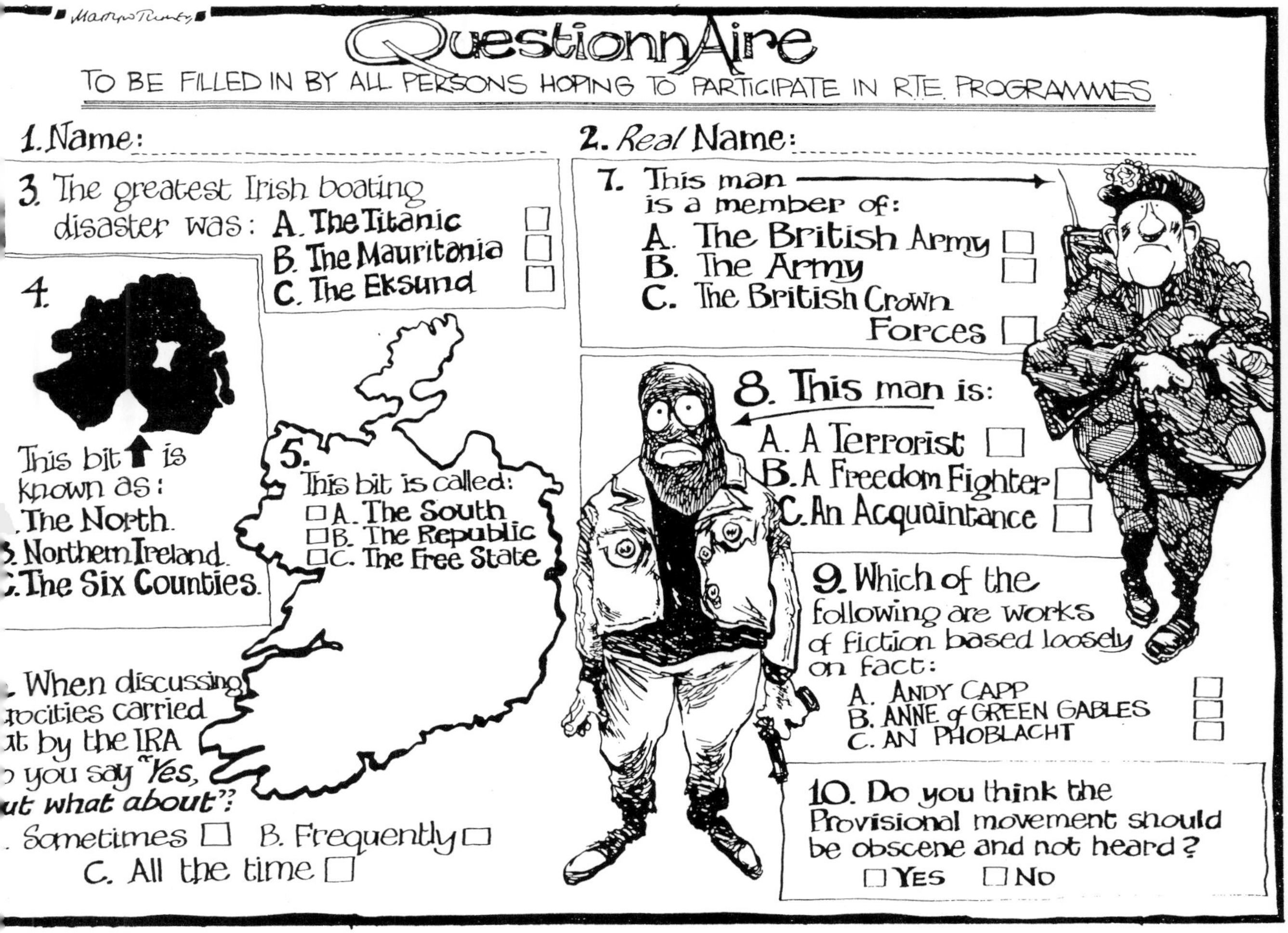
QuestionnAire
TO BE FILLED IN BY ALL PERSONS HOPING TO PARTICIPATE IN RTE PROGRAMMES
1. Name:
2. Real Name:
3. The greatest Irish boating disaster was:
A. The Titanic ☐
B. The Mauritania ☐
C. The Eksund ☐
4.
This bit ↑ is known as:
. The North.
. Northern Ireland.
. The Six Counties.
5.
This bit is called:
☐ A. The South
☐ B. The Republic
☐ C. The Free State
. When discussing
rocities carried
it by the IRA
you say "Yes,
ut what about"?
. Sometimes ☐
B. Frequently ☐
C. All the time ☐
7. This man →
is a member of:
A. The British Army ☐
B. The Army ☐
C. The British Crown Forces ☐
8. This man is:
A. A Terrorist ☐
B. A Freedom Fighter ☐
C. An Acquaintance ☐
9. Which of the following are works of fiction based loosely on fact:
A. ANDY CAPP ☐
B. ANNE of GREEN GABLES ☐
C. AN PHOBLACHT ☐
10. Do you think the Provisional movement should be obscene and not heard?
☐ YES
☐ NO

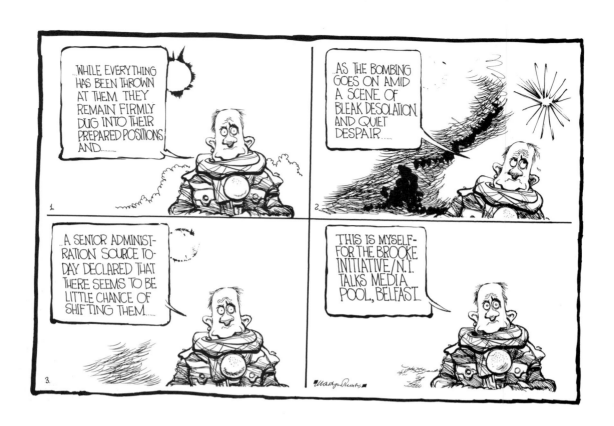

THE WORLD TODAY

In Nicaragua, after 7 years of fighting, they are about to agree a cease fire.

In Afghanistan, after 8 years of war, they are talking about what to do after the Russians go.

In N. Ireland, after almost 20 years of fighting, we are discussing the policing of future funerals.

This man may have
wanted to buy missiles
to kill people.....

He was a diplomat. He
got sent home....

This man might have sold
bits of missile and then
bought other things that
kill people....

He got thrown
in jail.....

This man designs, makes
and markets missiles
which kill people...

He's got The Queen's
Award for Industry....

94

Paris In The Spring

IRISH UNITY

IRATOLLAH

LEGITIMATE TARGETS: Some examples.

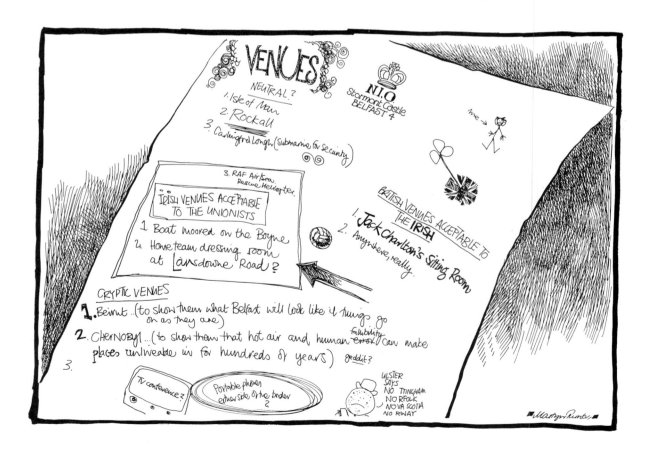

OUTBREAK OF "MAD LAW DISEASE" IN IRELAND

New Political Sayings No.35

Go to the country....

...before the country comes to you....

The Dail ....just dissolve. For headaches..!

The Latest Temptation of Charlie *

* WARNING: This could be a mildly controversial but basically boring entertainment.

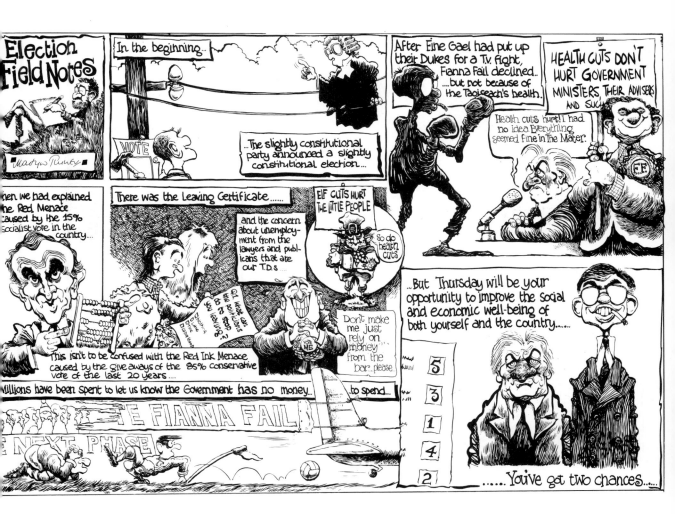

Athens

Dublin

The P.Ds want to survive...

The Left want to be a strong opposition...

F.G. want to share Government...

F.F. want total power....

The Election is only over a week and already our politicians are found wanting...

Martyn Turner

111

The President of Europe discusses with the Taoiseach of Ireland the European ideal, the Treaty of Rome and the free movement of goods.

..... Speaking of <u>Inner City</u> Vandalism.....

GOVERNMENT UNDERSPENDING — WORLDWIDE REACTION:

Nurse, London.   Teacher, Wagga Wagga.   Barman, New York.

VISIBILITY PROBLEMS IN PARTS OF DUBLIN - IS THE ANTI-SMOG LEGISLATION WORKING?

TEST PICTURES →

As seen in most of the country.......

As seen in Dublin West.......

123

HOW WE TRY TO GET TO THE PRESIDENCY....

124

NEWS ITEM: TURKEY DISCOVERS LOST IRISH MASTERPIECE

You have been part of a systematic reign of torture, violence, abuse and abduction.....

You now say you plan to give up some of these activities!

So we must find some way to reward you, Mister De Klerk...

ND of the COLD WAR : Things no longer needed...

Hardware   Munitions   Ironware

...Wouldn't it be nice if we could say the same about the people we sell them to....

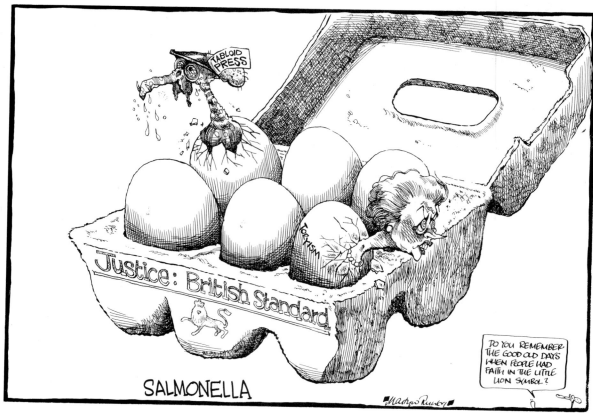

SALMONELLA

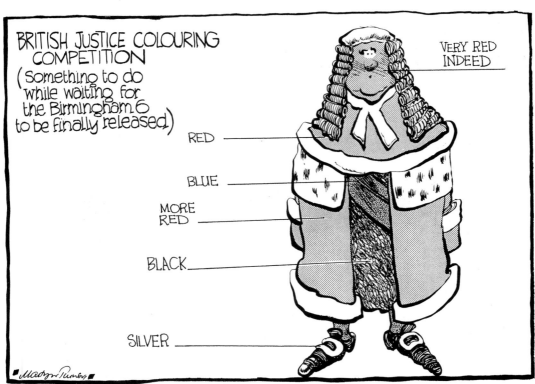

UNSTOPPABLE
GULF OIL FLOW

DOWNSTREAM POLLUTION

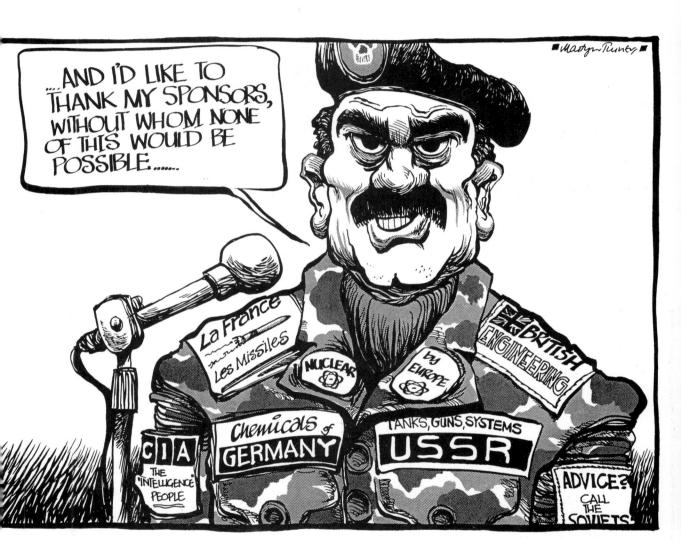

GULF WAR
PEACE PLAN

OLIVE
BRANCH

ARMS LIMITATION
AGREEMENTS

NOBEL
PEACE
PRIZE

BALTIC STATES

REACTION

SHARE
PRICES

THE
MARKETS

154

JAN 1ST 1991

IRAQ

MARCH 1ST 1991

March 1991.

The freedom of Kuwait, the return of the Government and the restoration of one man, one vote.......

.....and this is the man who has that one vote..